To my Friends at The Children's Place: Thank you for your vision to bring more than just great clothes to children, but also to make a difference in their lives with imagination, stories, and fun activities. You're shifting the paradigm for clothing retailers. Thanks for your support and the opportunity to touch the lives of children and their families and believing in what I do.

To Douglas: What a wild ride! Whether it's a roller coaster, Ferris wheel, bumper cars, or the carousel – you're the one I want by my side. Thanks for always being right there, even when we both need to grip the bar extra tight.

To Jared and Cameron: Thanks for letting me live in the world of your imagination with you. There is nothing better than playing dress-up, dancing in the rain, painting our faces, or howling at the moon with the two of you. You are the MAGIC in my life!

To the M&M's in my life, Mom and Michele: Your constant support on this project was off the charts. Who else could I call all hours of the night to discuss anything from an adjective to a rhyme...to life?

To Karin: Thanks for bringing CiCi and Ace and all the other zany little characters I have floating around in my head to life.

To Zenon: Thank you for bringing my words to life, too. You are a graphics wizard!

I Love You All, Rainey

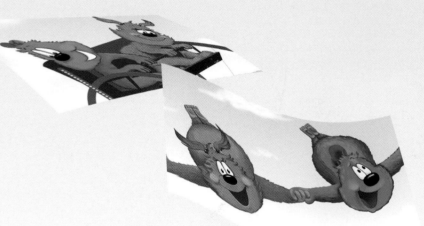

Exclusively Produced for
The Children's Place
by DreamDog Press
3686 King Street, Suite 160
Alexandria, VA 22302

Order online @ **www.childrensplace.com**

Cataloging-in-Publication Data
Rainey (aka Friedman, Lorraine Lee.)
Ferris Wheel Fun/ by Rainey; illustrated by Karin Huggens – 1st ed.
p.cm.

SUMMARY: CiCi and Ace go on a Ferris wheel ride where their imagination takes them: soaring with birds, diving under the sea, digging in the ground with some friendly moles, blasting into space to meet a new friend and many more exciting adventures . The book shows the power of a child's imagination to create their reality. Included is a music CD with original songs, Imagination Note and Family Art Activity.

ISBN: 0-9666199-8-6
1. imagination—juvenile fiction. 2. brother and sister adventure—Juvenile fiction
3. exploring – Juvenile fiction.
I. Huggens, Karin II.Title

Ferris Wheel Fun!

A MAGIC Ride

by

Rainey

Illustrated by
Karin Huggens

I see the faces way below.

My little sister
looks so small.

And hey,
I see our shopping mall.

THE CHILDREN'S
PLACE

from being *way,* Way up high.
I feel that I can touch the sky.

And now I know why birds soar
'cause with each turn, I want some more.

More air, more clouds -- they all pass by
and I pretend that I can *fly.*

We land safely in our seat
with our view that can't be beat.

"Pilot to CiCi,
do you read me?"

Ace asks
into his
walkie-talkie.

I play along with some finesse
and look for the red button to press.

"Crrr – there's static on the line, but don't worry, I'm just fine."

Then, there's a **VROOM...VROOM**
sound I hear
and we put our seat into gear.

Now it's a racecar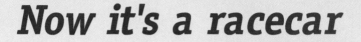

*ZOOM*ing by.

It goes so fast that **it can** **fly.**

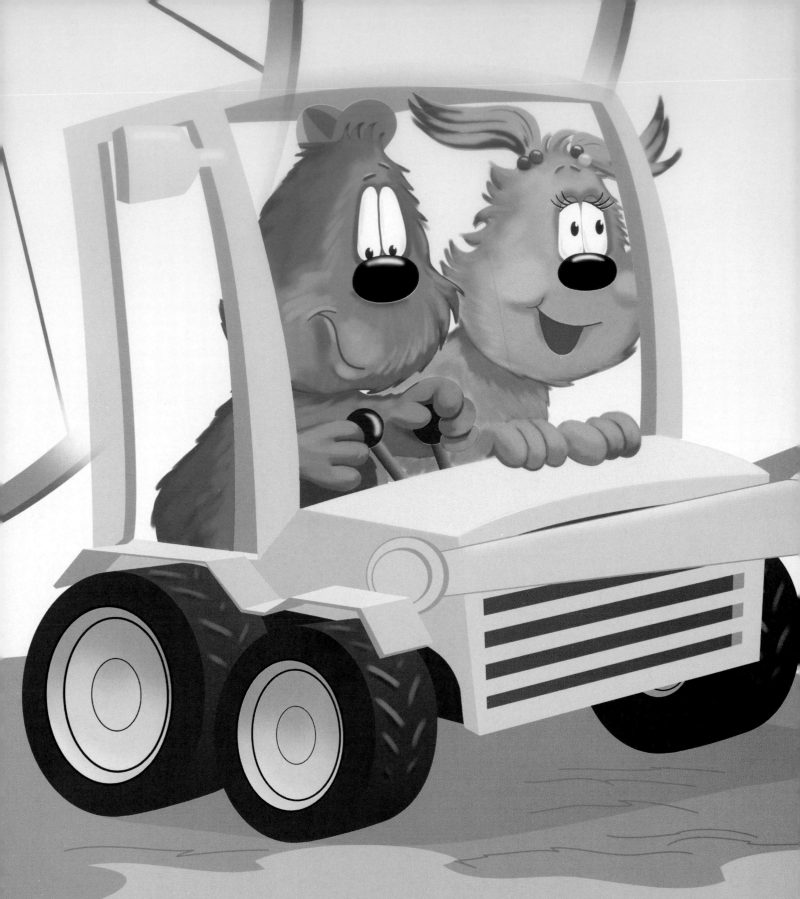

Next we're in some sort of rig
plunging into the earth to dig.

We dig like moles into the ground while making a "***whirrr-whizzz***" kind of sound.

Down in the dirt,
we explore and play
meeting funny bugs
who wiggle our way.

Earthworms, grubs and even slugs and lots of little smiling bugs.

Something starts pulling and we rise up again

I say, "How about a ride
on a rocket ship?"

And, we both hold the bar
with a tighter grip

Then our Ferris wheel
dives straight down

like a deep sea submarine underground.

We talk about the creatures
that we see
underwater,
my best friend and me.

There's an octopus and anemone

and a strange fish
staring up at me.

We go deeper where it's dark.

"Hey, I think I see a SHARK!"

Up we rise,

back to level ground

and we both take a look around.

It's so beautiful
way up high –
the clouds,
the air
and blue,
blue sky.

Sadly,

the ride starts to slow

and my brother and I both know

this adventure has come to an end,

but another one
will soon begin.

The really cool thing that I find
is I can go there with my mind.
Anytime I want to ride,
all I have to do is look inside.

So, I don't really need a fair.
My imagination can take me there.
My creativity holds the key --
All those fun ideas come from

ME!

Using Imagination with Your Child

Imagination brings the carnival into daily life. It has the power to change a cardboard box into a racecar, a fork into a microphone for performing songs, and a pinecone into a walkie-talkie. CiCi and Ace could have sat back to ride the Ferris wheel, but instead they expanded this fun experience into something dynamic and exciting. They chose to live in the powerful world of their imagination where reality can transform into a magical world.

Our children enrich their lives by tapping into their own natural resource – their imagination. And, we can be their guides. Here are some suggestions for encouraging and nurturing your child's imagination:

- **Don't be limited by what is...imagine what could be.** Albert Einstein, one of the greatest thinkers of our time said, "Imagination is more important than knowledge." Knowledge provides the facts of what is known while imagination creates new experiences and ultimately new knowledge. Believe in the realm of possibilities...for you and your children.
- **Create a space within your home where children can be free to explore the world of their imagination.** Let them be free to create their own alternative reality. It's fun and they'll be living in "the real world" soon enough. Children need to be able to act silly without having their exuberance judged. Let them be as funny and goofy as they want. Give them space to create, whether it's for building a fort, dressing as a princess or Super Hero, or creating an area for performing. You are sending the message that their creative play is valued and encouraged by you.
- **Allow and encourage experimentation** – experimenting is one of the ways children come to understand their world. You may not know that the pile of blocks was a city or their stuffed animals spread on the table were assorted for selling in their pretend store, so don't be so quick to clean up their creations. Ask them to explain what they've made, praise their originality and vision, play for a while – then you can clean it up, together.
- **Use art as a creative means of expression.** It is another language by which children can communicate. If they did something nice for a friend, ask them to draw a picture of it and put it up on their wall to remind them of how proud you are of their good behavior. Use art as another way to talk to your children. Have paper, crayons, paints and other materials available for all their wonderful creations.
- **Sing, dance and play together.** Put on music after dinner, first thing in the morning, or anytime and dance around together. Dance like a butterfly...then a dragon... then a kangaroo, and whatever else pops into their minds. Make up silly songs, even with imaginary words or languages.
- **Be a model for your children.** Play imagination games together. Here's an easy example: pick different things to be/act out together – a jellyfish, an eagle, a dinosaur, a snake, a kitten...the list goes on and on. Ask your child to come up with creatures and then transform yourself into their imaginary world. Or, just play with their favorite toys. You will be amazed at how much you can learn about your child's world from playing with dolls or Super Heroes.

Imagination leads to strong, empowered children who feel free to decide for themselves because they are accustomed to being creators of their own world. Children should be free to choose what they want to play – it creates a sense of self. Using child-directed games and play teaches our children how to make decisions and sends the message, "I value what you want to do or be."

Imagination isn't just for children; it enriches the lives of adults, as well. You have the perfect teachers to help you nurture your own imagination, your children. Allow imagination to lead you and your children to an even richer life together.

Interactive Family Art Activity
Create a Family and Friends Ferris Wheel

Doing art projects together is as important as playing together. It enables your children to express and connect with the imaginative, creative part of themselves. Doing interactive art projects together builds self-esteem; there is no right or wrong way to create.

This art project can be done at any age, and its complexity and detail will vary based on the age of the "artist." You can follow these simple instructions, or use your imagination and own creative touches to make it your unique creation. And visit us at www.childrensplace.com for more ideas.

You will need:

- Poster Board – any color
- Markers, crayons or paints – you chose (washable is always a good idea)
- Different colors of construction paper
- Pictures of family and friends
- Glue

Step 1
On your poster board, draw a large circle.
In the center of your circle, draw a small circle.
From that small circle, draw lines connecting to the large circle.
It will look like a large wheel with lots of spokes from the center.

Step 2
Using the construction paper, cut out different colored rectangles.
Glue each rectangle to the spoke part of the big circle.
You've just created the seats/buckets on the Ferris wheel.
(Older children can design each seat and give it a different flair.
One can have smiley faces, one can have flowers, glitter –
there's no end to the possibilities and style you can create.)

Step 3
Glue or tape pictures of family members or friends into each seat.

Step 4
You can write your family members names on the seat (if they are not decorated) or just under each seat.
Then, for the older kids, add thought bubbles with funny expressions or their favorite things to say. For instance, grandma's might say: "I love my Little Man!" and big sisters' could say, "Way cool!" or "You go, girl!" Bring the people you love to life with their favorite sayings.

Step 5
At the top of the poster write in fun big letters "FAMILY and FRIENDS Ferris Wheel" or give it your own creative title. (Older children may try doing it in glitter or cut out each letter from a magazine and paste them together to get your title).

Step 6
Tell a story using your poster. Make up your own version of "Ferris Wheel Fun" starring your family. Make it as whimsical and funny as you want. You are the storyteller; you are the creator.

Have fun! Be as creative as you can be...
This is your work of art...your work of heart!

Up...up...up I go...

Up...up...up I go...
And I see the faces way below.
Up...up...up I go...
for some *Ferris Wheel Fun*.

I want to reach out my hands and fly. (2 claps)
You can do it -- touch the sky.
Side by side, we can glide
on our Ferris wheel ride.

We're climbin' higher, higher still.
This ride is oh, such a thrill.
Let's pretend we're in a plane
flying through the pourin' rain.

(Children make sound effects of a plane.)

Now, it's a racecar zoomin' by.
We're going so fast – we can fly.
Push the peddle to the ground,
and watch us racin' all around.

(Make sound effects of a car racing by.)

Down...Down underground
and the ride keeps turnin' round and round.
Down...Down underground
for more *Ferris Wheel Fun*!

I want to dig down in a hole,
and burrow like a mole.
Look at all the cool bugs.
I think I touched a slug.
Uuuh! Time for us to go.

Up...up...up we go...
And we see the faces way below.
Up...up...up we go...
for some *Ferris Wheel Fun*.

Now, it's rocket ship into space.
We're gonna win the rocket race.
Blasting through all the stars
and landing on the planet Mars.

(Boogie to Funny Martian music.)

And, then we meet Za-ru-pee
who invites us home for tea.
But on our very first sip,
the rocket ship starts to dip
Ut- oh! Time to go! (Za-ru-pee says this.)

Down...Down underground
and the ride keeps turnin' round and round.
Down...Down underground
for more *Ferris Wheel Fun*!

Now, we're in a deep sea submarine,
a really cool underwater machine.
There is so much we can see
and lots of strange fish looking up at me.

We go deeper where it's dark
Oh, I think see a SHARK!

Up...up...up we go...
and the ride it starts to really slow.
Then we rise back to the ground
and both take a look around.

It's really cool what you can do
with all the fun ideas inside you.
So, any time you want a magic ride,
just take a look inside.

(Singing together)
(Ace) Up...up...up I go...
(CiCi) I want to reach out my hands and fly. (2 claps)

(Ace) I see the faces way below. (CiCi) You can do it -- touch the sky.

(Ace) Up...up...up I go... (CiCi) Side by side, we can glide

(Ace) For some *Ferris Wheel Fun*. (CiCi) On our Ferris wheel ride.

Ferris Wheel...
Ferris Wheel...
Ferris Wheel Fun!

CiCi: Want to ride again?
Ace: Oh, yeah!

It's All Up to You and Me

(Spoken) CiCi: Cool... this is a magic ride!
Ace: Magic?
CiCi: Yea, anytime you use your imagination, it's magic.
Ace: What do you mean?
CiCi: OK, when we go up, imagine this...

Do like the birds do and soar through the air.
Laugh as you feel the cool wind in your hair.
Being so high you can see way below.
But, it's up to you, where you should go.

So, follow your heart, your dreams and your mind.
Don't worry at all what you've left behind.
See, you can be anything you want to be...
It's all up to you and me.

So, if you're a bird,
you should fly so high.
Spread your wings and touch the sky.

Then, make the most beautiful singing sound,
so all of the people will gather around.
And you smile on high as you pass them by
and say, "It's ME!"

Ace: Whooo! That was fun!
But, what do we do when the ride goes down?
CiCi: Hmmm...I have some ideas, but it's your turn.
Use your imagination, what would you be?
Ace: Ha! I know....

Do like the fish do and swim all about,
or be a big whale blowing water from your spout.
Being so deep you can see far and wide.
Now it's your turn to look deep inside.

So, follow your heart, your dreams and your mind.
Don't worry at all what you've left behind.
See, you can be anything you want to be...
It's all up to you and me.
So, if you're a fish,
you can wave a fin,
or wiggle your tail with a big grin.

Then splash all about so the people would shout,
"I just saw a flying fish.
Oh, come make a wish."
Then jump up again, waving your fin,
and say, "It's Me!"

And, if we were eagles,
well think how we could soar.
And if we were lions,
imagine the sound we'd roar.

All the fun things to do — inside me and in you.
We'll be the best me for the whole world to see.
We'll smile so proud and then shout it out loud,
waving our hands — oh, the fun never ends...
And say, "It's ME!"

So, follow your heart, your dreams and your mind.
Don't worry at all what you've left behind.
See, you can be anything you want to be...
It's all up to you, (Ace)
It's all up to you, (CiCi)
It's all up to you and me. (together)

Zinka-Linka-Choo

Hey, my name is Za-ru-pee,
and I'd like to have you home for tea.
I saw you shooting through the stars
and landing here on planet Mars.
I made a wish for a friend, you see.
And now, you're here to play with me.
I know about you from Martian schools.
One thing's for sure: The Children's Place rules.

Say Za (Za) – [CiCi and Ace answer his chant]
Say Ru (Ru)
Say Pee (Pee)
(Giggles)
It's not funny – it's my name.

We have a custom that we do;
it's our way to say "hello" to you.
On earth you call it a happy dance.
You jump around and even prance.
But here on Mars it's a Zinka-linka-choo.
I'd like to do it with both of you.
It may sound funny, but give it a try.
Shake your bootie and wave your hands in the sky.
Now stomp your feet and clap your hands.
Pretend you're playin' music in a rock 'n roll band.

Now wiggle your hips side to side,
and pretend you're on a magic carpet ride.

Say Ooooh! (Ooooh!)
Say Laaaa! (Laaaa!)
All together now...
Oh –La-La!
I knew you'd like it.

Hey, my name's CiCi and this is Ace.
This is our first time in outer space.
Thanks for the welcome and "howdy-do."
It's really fun meeting you.
I can't believe we've come so far,
just playing a game in our Ferris wheel car.
Imagination is a powerful thing.
It kinda makes me want to sing.

Zinka-linka-choo
Zinka-linka-choo.
Watch all the cool moves I can do.
(Za-ru-pee) You go, girl!

My name's Ace – this is way cool.
Can't wait to tell my friends at school.
Sometimes we pretend to be you.
Now I can say it with a Zinka-linka-choo.
I'll teach all my friends your special dance.
They'll move like ants are in their pants.
Now, let me teach you some of our zingers
High 5, Thumbs up and makin' peace fingers.

Say Peace, Za-ru-pee
Say Peace to you.
Now I can say it with a Zinka-linka-choo.
It may sound funny, but give it a try.
Shake your bootie and wave your hands in the sky.
Now stomp your feet and clap your hands.
Pretend you're playin' music in a rock 'n roll band.
Now wiggle your hips side to side,
and pretend you're on a magic carpet ride.

Now, I know we're all the same
even though you have a really strange name.
We like to play, sing and dance like you.
Now we can do it with a Zinka-Linka-Choo.
You taught us your cool Martian jive,
and you taught me peace and high five. (Za-ru-pee)
That's what you do with all your friends --
you give and share and the party never ends.
So before we have to say good-bye,
let's all give it one more try.

Zinka-Linka-Choo...
Zinka-Linka-Choo...
Watch us now, we can do it, too!

It may sound funny, but give it a try.
Shake your bootie and wave your hands in the sky.
Now stomp your feet and clap your hands.
Pretend you're playin' music in a rock 'n roll band.
Now wiggle your hips side to side,
and pretend you're on a magic carpet ride.

And, say Zinka (Zinka)
Linka (Linka)
Choo (Choo)

I love you!